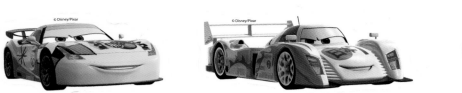

READY FOR TAKEOFF

Phidal

Meet the Planes

These planes love flying through the sky. Match your stickers to the shadows to find out who they are.

BRAVO

ECHO

EL CHUPACABRA

RIPSLINGER

SKIPPER

DUSTY

The Right Number

The world of planes is filled with all sorts of things! Use your stickers to complete the rows, and then count up the items.

6

7

8

9

10

Flying High

The planes are very excited. They are about to take flight. Use your stickers to fill this sky scene with some aerial action.

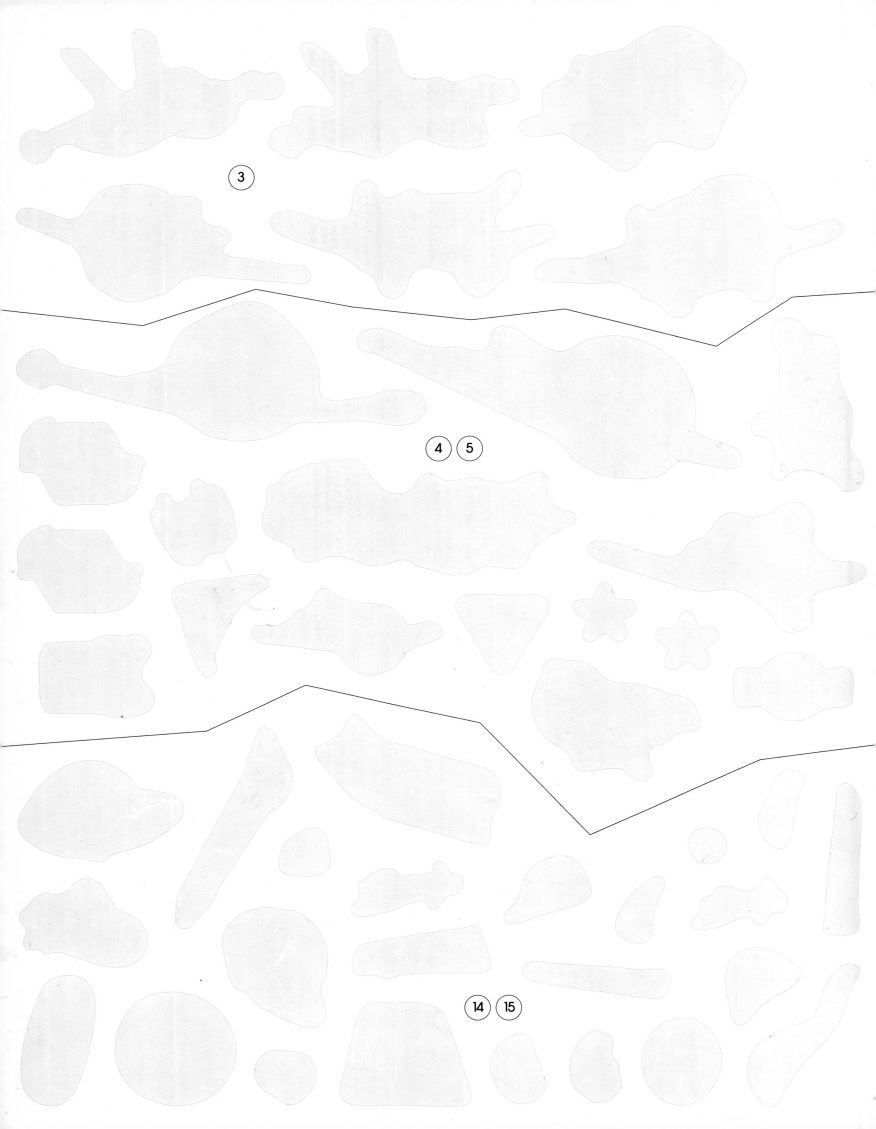

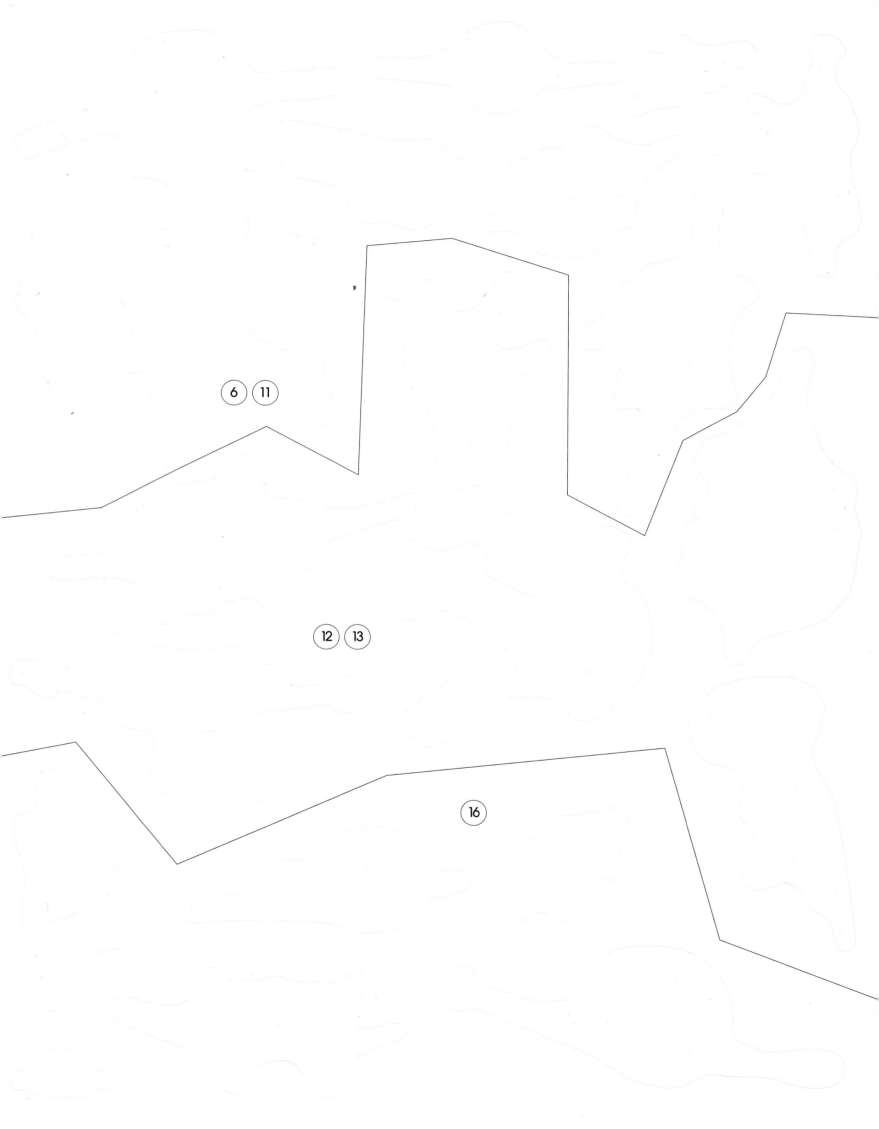

From Close-up

Can you recognize these planes from their close-ups? Match your stickers to the shadows to reveal who they are.

Top Form

These planes need to be in tip-top shape for their aerial adventure. Use your stickers to fill in the missing parts.

Runway Repeat

These planes are coming in for a landing! Use your stickers to recreate the top scene in the bottom one.

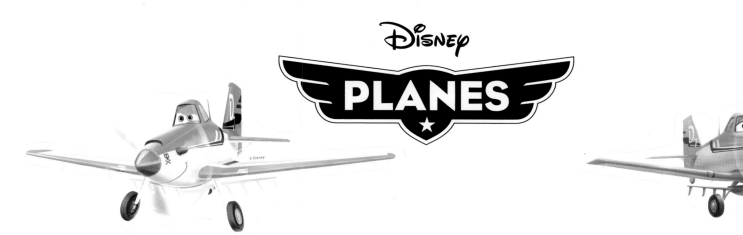

HIGH IN THE SKY

Phidal

World Tour

Each of the planes has a place they like to call home. Match your stickers to the shadows to find out where the planes are from.

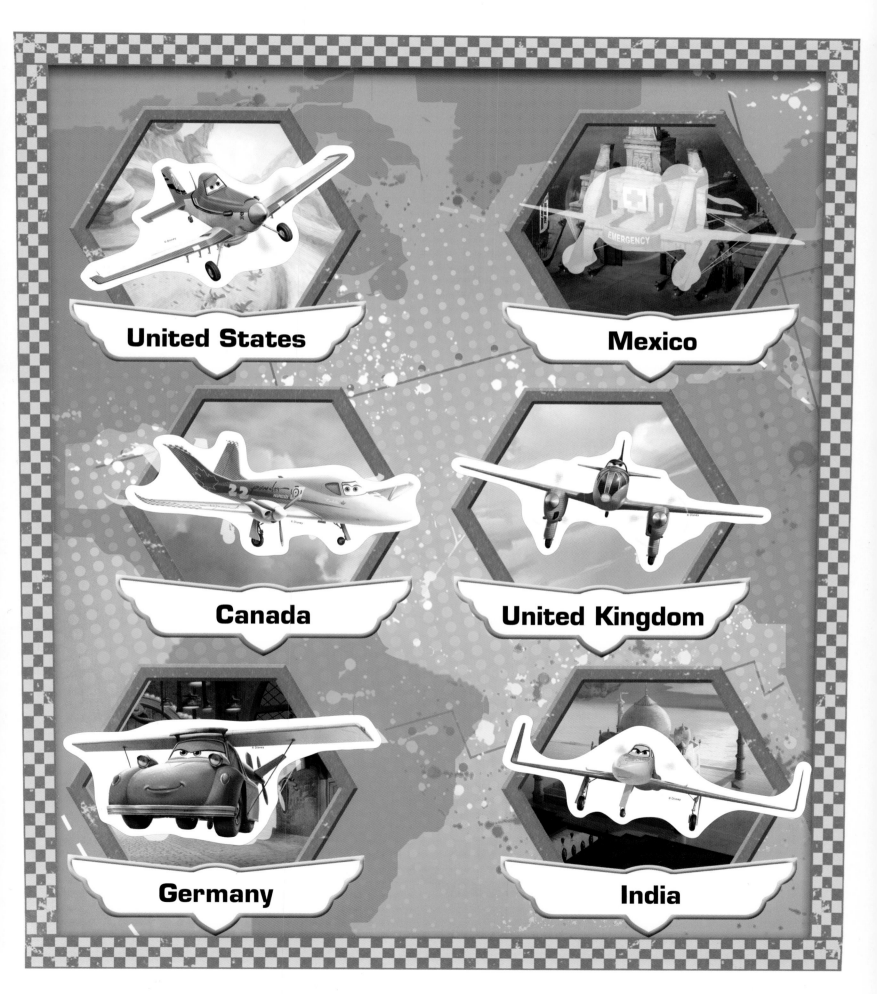

United States

Mexico

Canada

United Kingdom

Germany

India

Planes, Cars, and Trucks!

The skies and roads are filled with different vehicles—some that fly and some that don't!
Use your stickers to complete the patterns below.

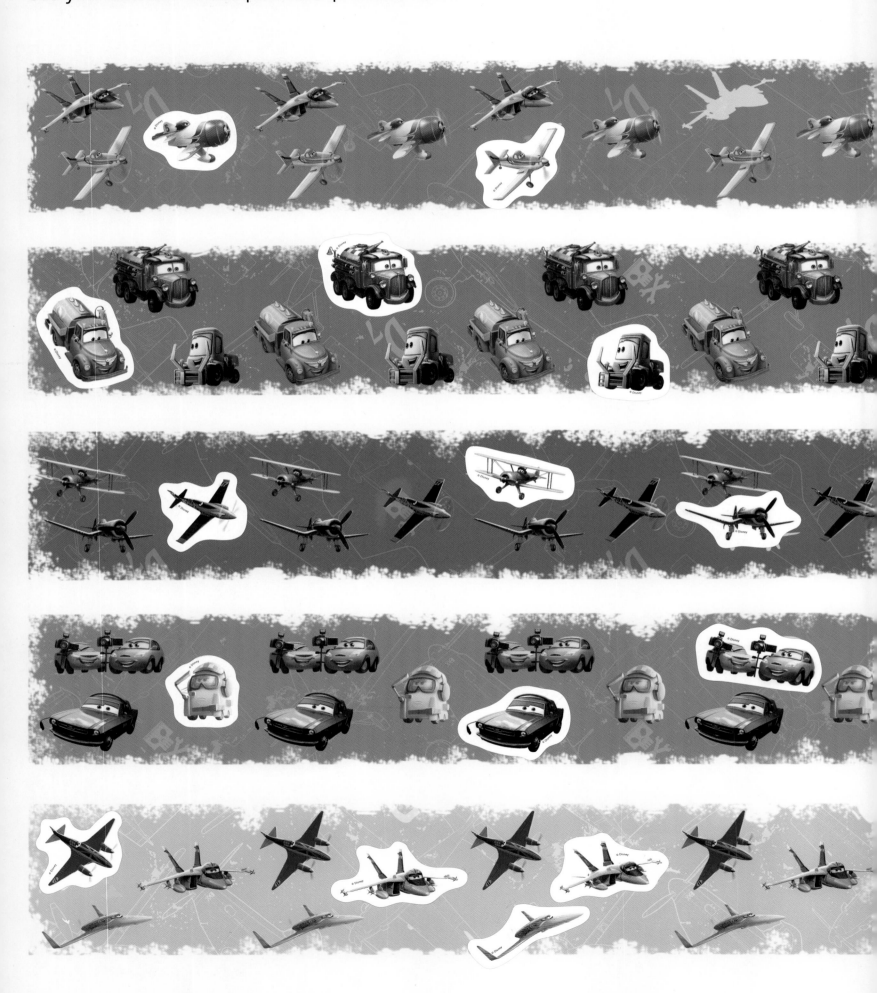

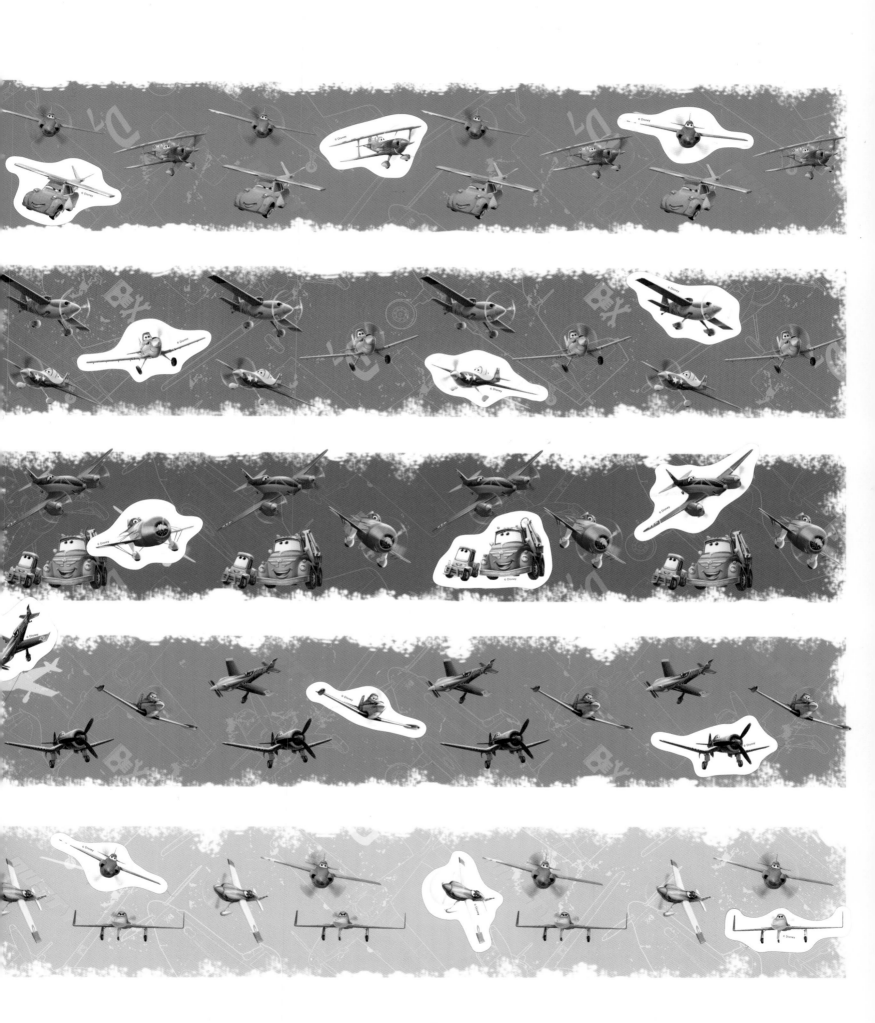

Desert Skies

This desert landscape is an exciting place to fly—but it isn't without its obstacles.
Use your stickers to show the planes flying through the scene.

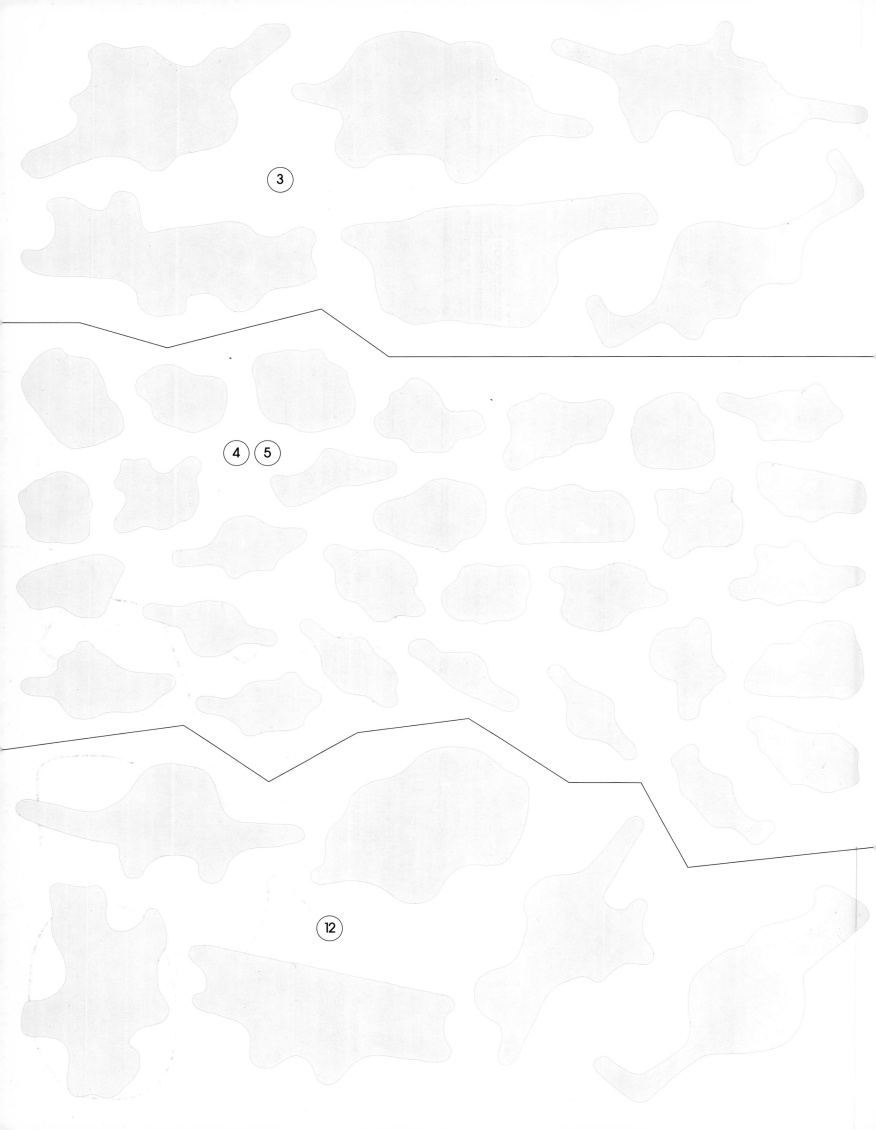

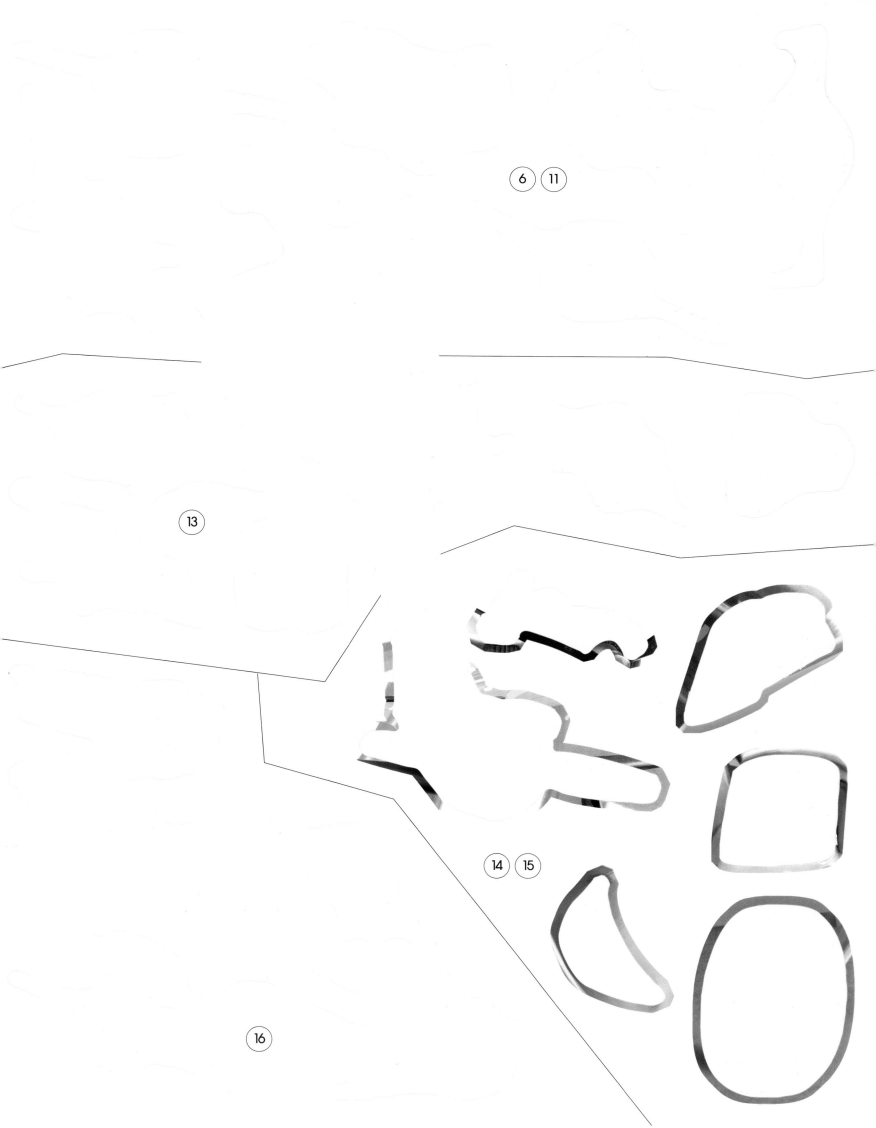

True Colors

These planes are each painted in their own special colors. Match your stickers to the shadows to see which plane goes with which colors.

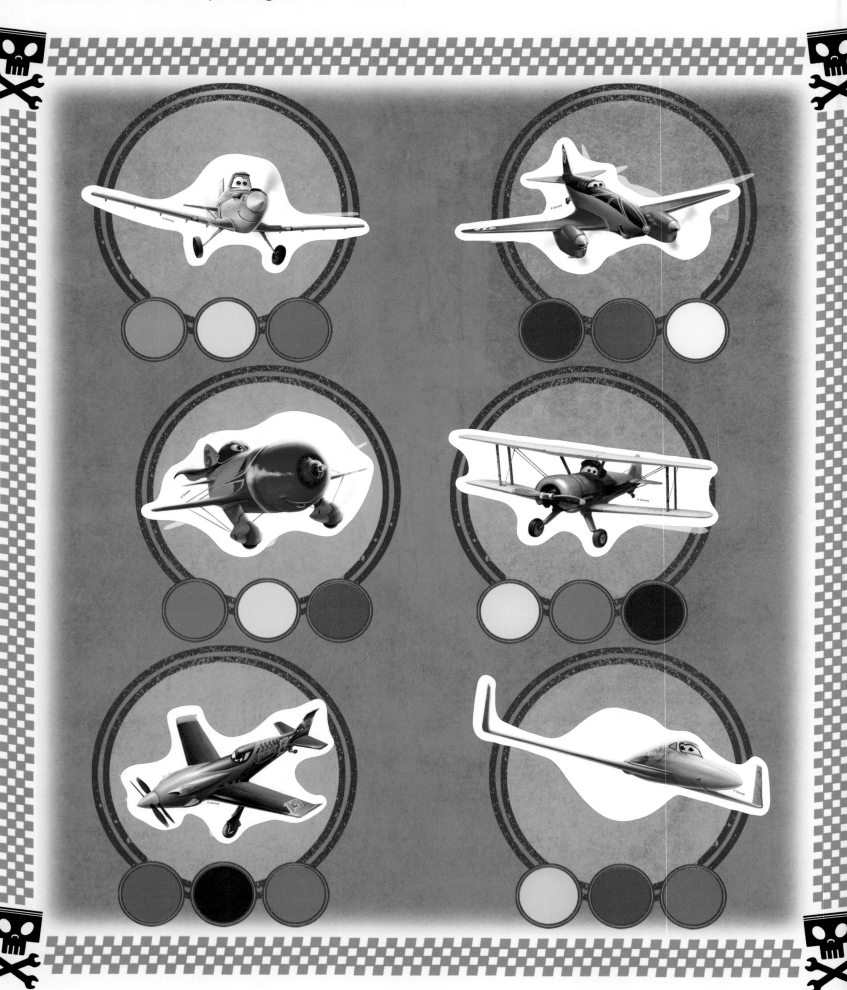

Opposites

Although the Planes characters are all vehicles, they are each unique—sometimes even opposite. Match your stickers to the shadows.

Down/Up

Fast/Slow

Left/Right

Small/Big

Old/New

One/Many

Fan Appeal!

Ready for a celebration, these vehicles need to look their best. Complete the image using your stickers.

Flying Team

These planes are very skilled at flying in formation. Use your stickers to recreate the top scene in the bottom one.

AROUND THE WORLD

Phidal

Fill 'n' Fly

Chug and Dottie are Dusty's biggest supporters. Use your stickers to help them get him ready for flying.

Air Race!

The Wings Around the Globe Rally puts Dusty to the test. Use your stickers to recreate some of the air race action!

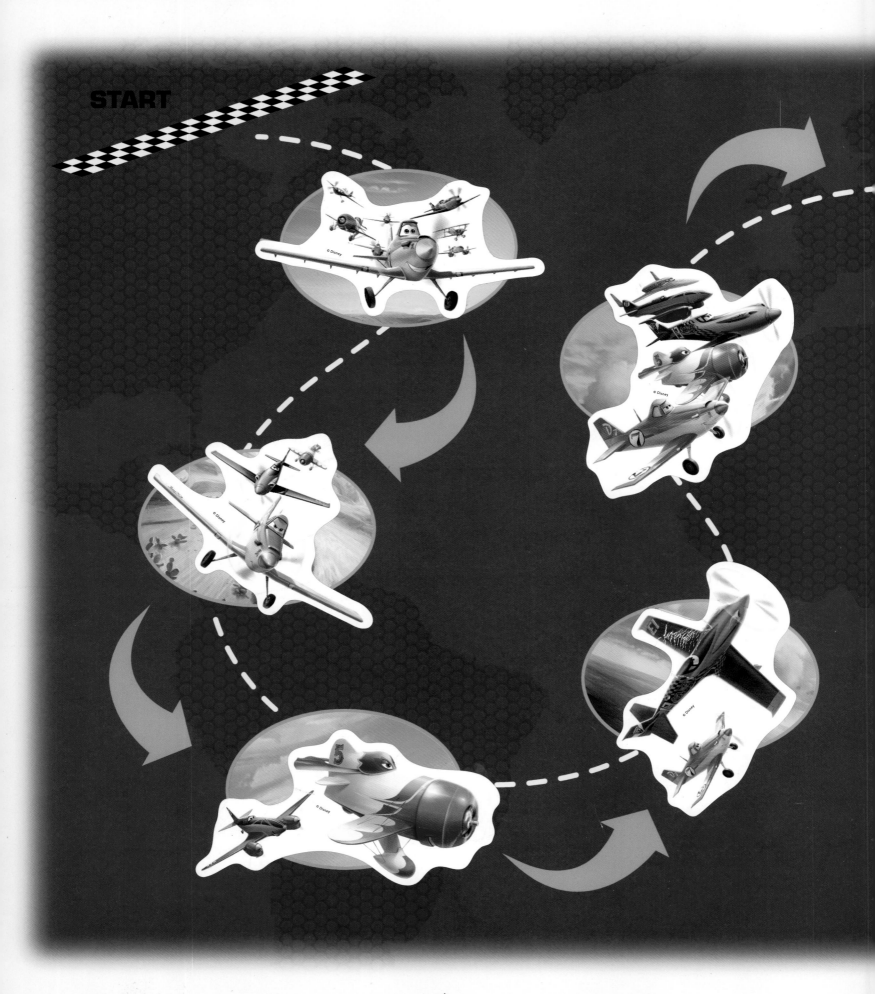

START

FINISH

Finish Line

The stadium is packed for the big finish. With your stickers show what order the planes arrive in as they get to the end of the race.

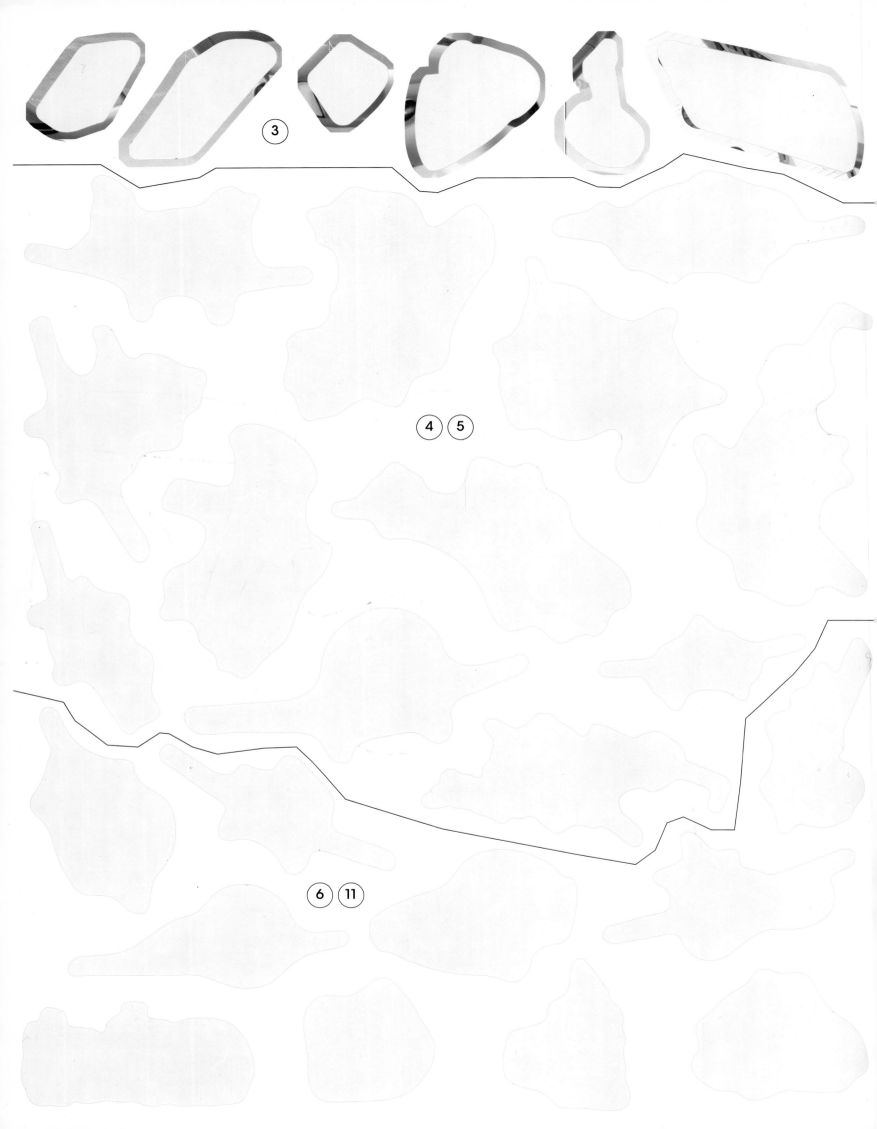

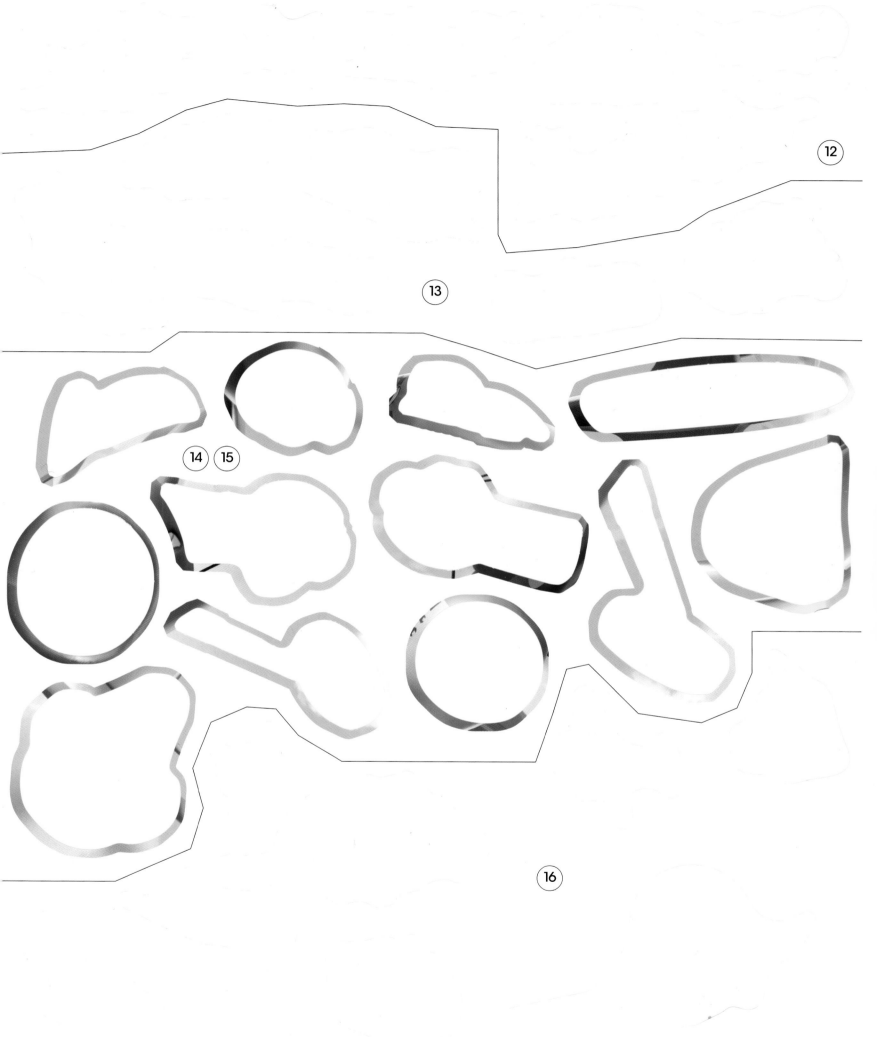

Add It Up

Match your stickers to the shadows, and then add up the number of aircraft and vehicles in each row.

Take Away

Match your stickers to the shadows, and then do the subtractions in each row to see how many aircraft and vehicles are left.

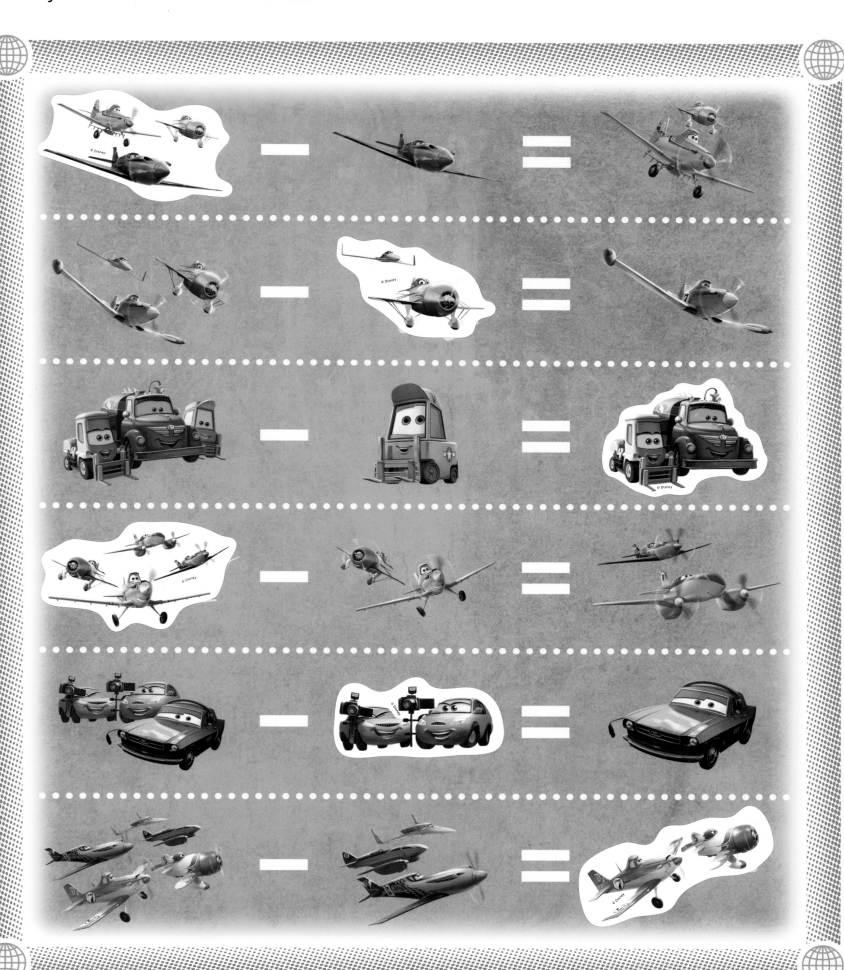

Racing Rivals

Who will win the race? These planes will need all the help they can get to make it to the finish line. Use your stickers to fill in their missing parts.

Fill Up Time

When gas is what they need, the planes head over to the Fill 'n' Fly. Use your stickers to recreate the top scene in the bottom one.

GOOD GUYS, BAD GUYS

2015 Produced and Published by Phidal Publishing, Inc.
All rights reserved.
www.phidal.com

Have fun decorating this scene with your stickers!

Racing Colors

Use your stickers to match each car to the right paint colors.

Teaming Up

Pair up these cars by placing your stickers over the shadows.

Lightning

Mater

Sarge

Fillmore

Luigi

Guido

Ramone

Flo

Holley

Finn

Giuseppe

Francesco

Grem

Acer

Okuni

Kingpin

Welcome to Paris

Decorate this beautiful Paris scene with your stickers.

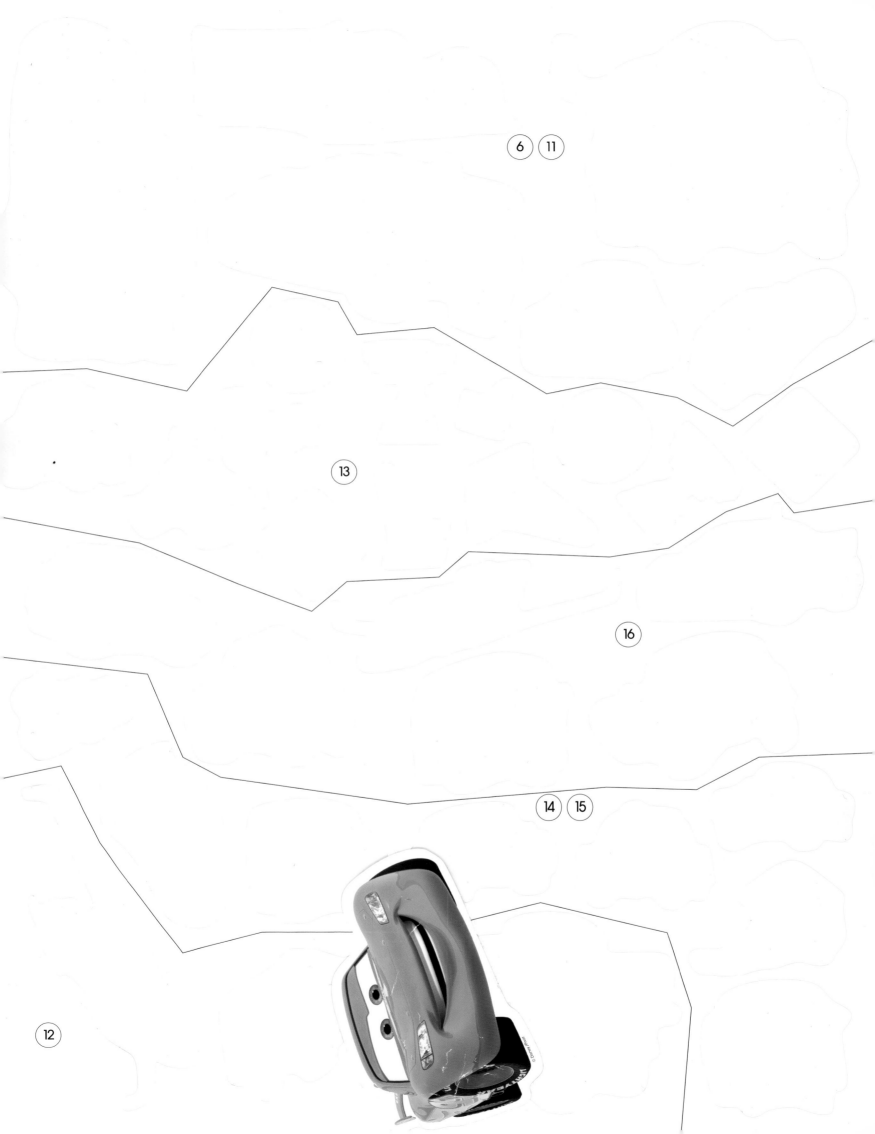

The Good, the Bad, and the Crew

Use your stickers to put the vehicles in the correct groups.

Who are the secret agents?

Who are the bad guys?

Who is the pit crew?

Countdown

Place your stickers over the shadows to get the right number in each box.

2 4

6 5

7 3

Mater Pays a Visit

Mater is off to meet Holley, but he sees some cars along the way. Who are they?

Guess Who?

Match the characters with their names by placing your stickers on their silhouettes.

Acer

Luigi

Max Schnell

Siddeley

Tomber

Fillmore

GRAND PRIX ADVENTURES

2015 Produced and Published by Phidal Publishing, Inc.
All rights reserved.
www.phidal.com

Have fun decorating this scene with your stickers!

Pit Stop Patterns

Complete these patterns with the help of your stickers.

Start Your Engines

Can you identify each of these cars? Place your stickers over the shadows.

Shu Todoroki

Jeff Gorvette

Lightning McQueen

Francesco Bernoulli

Rip Clutchgoneski

Miguel Camino

Max Schnell

Raoul ÇaRoule

Secret Agents

Place each car above the right name using your stickers.

Tow Mater

Holley Shiftwell

Finn McMissile

Rod "Torque" Redline

It's a Piazza Party!

The cars visit Luigi and Guido's hometown! Decorate the scene using your stickers.

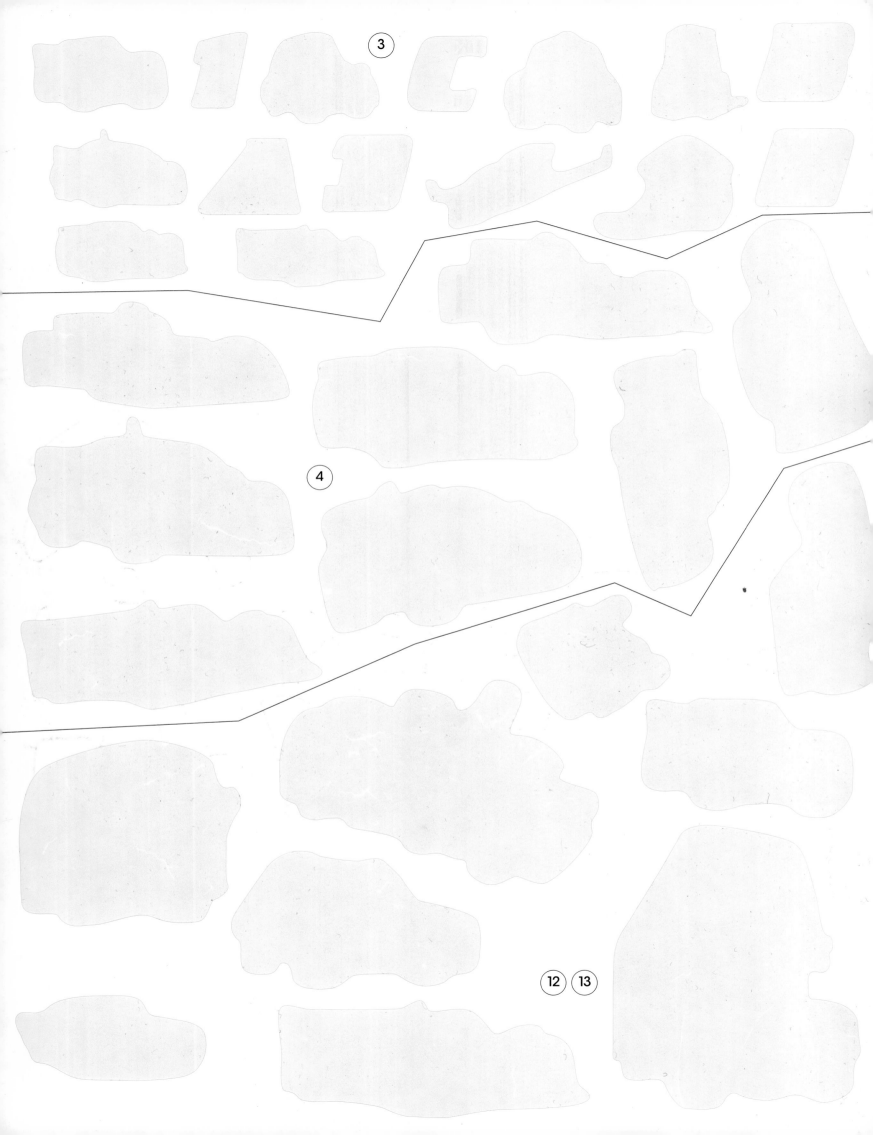

5

6 11

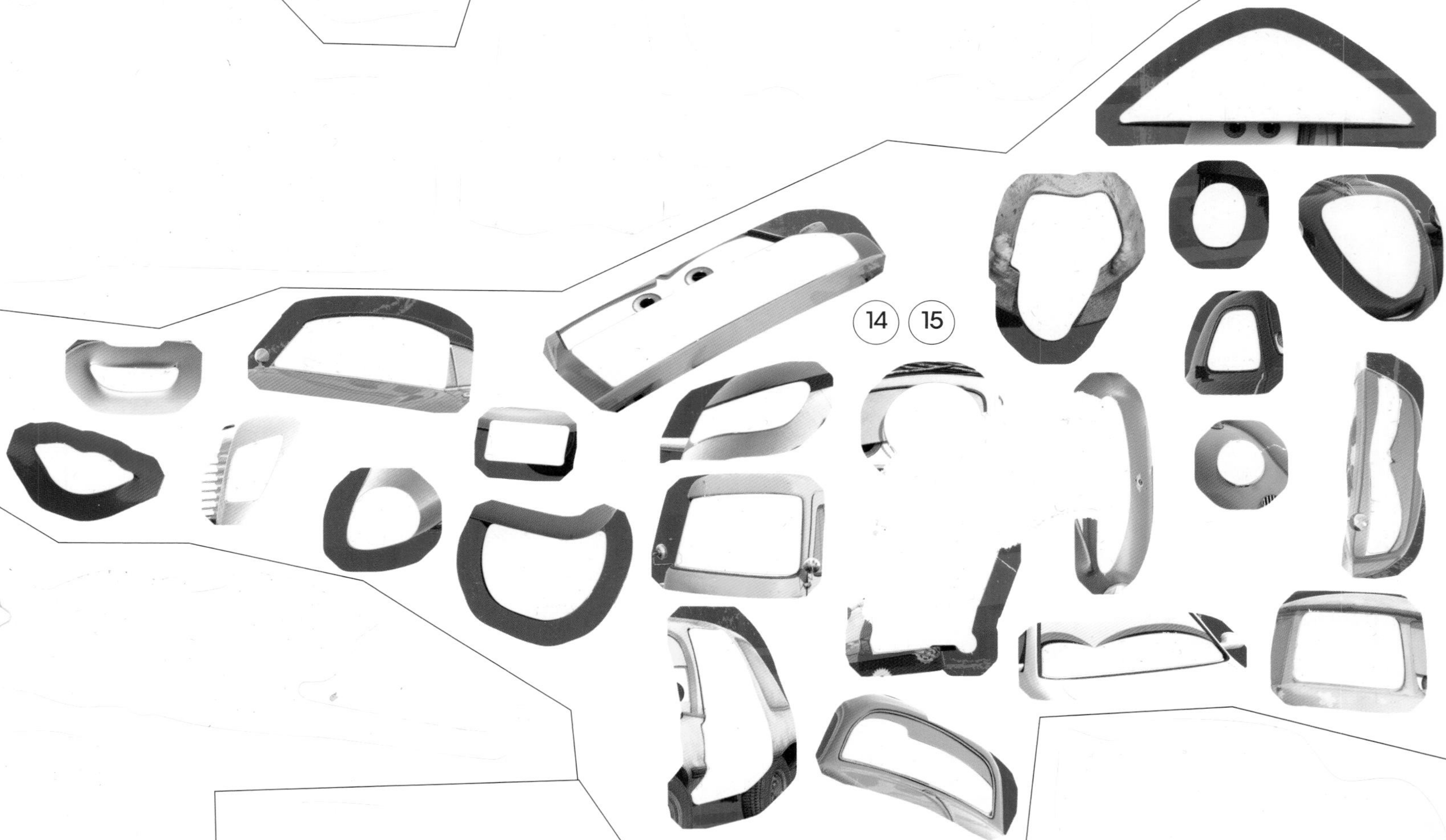

14 15

16

12 13

Car Opposites

The cars need your help to solve these opposites with your stickers.

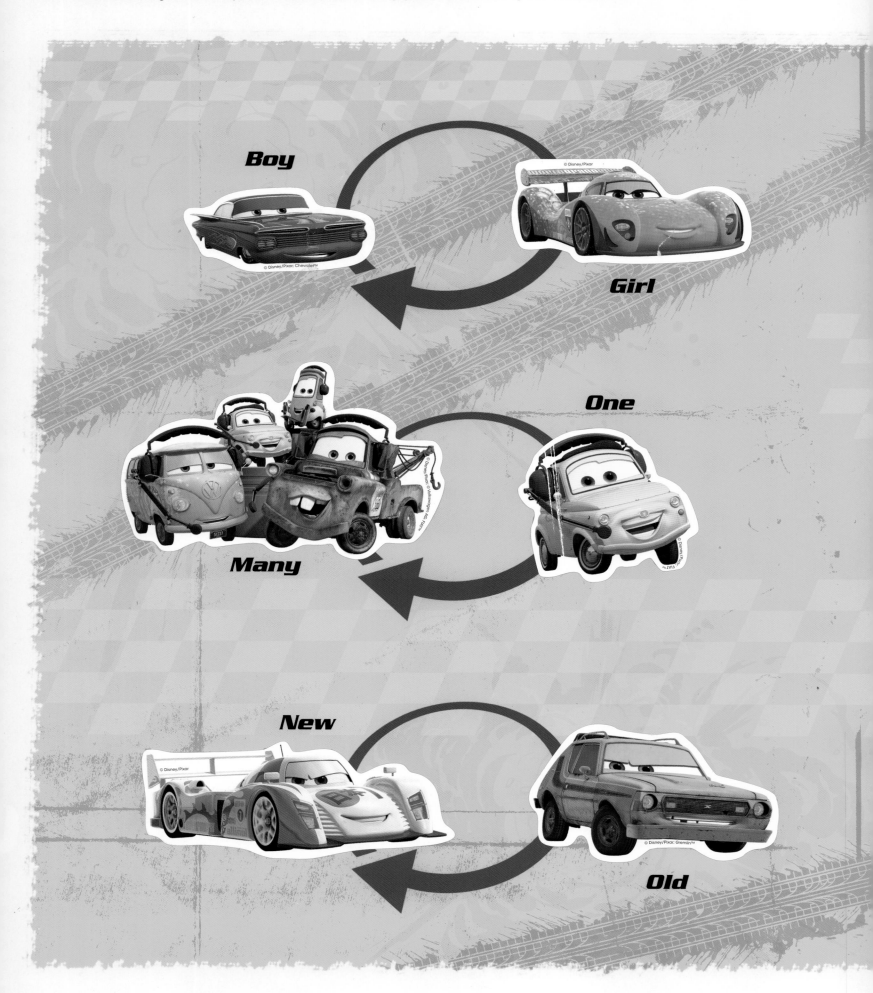

Boy

Girl

One

Many

New

Old

Plain

Fancy

Small

Big

Awake

Sleepy

Missing Parts

Place the parts over the right shadows to complete these characters.

Behind the Scenes

Use your stickers to match the race cars to the right crew members.

SECRET MISSION

2015 Produced and Published by Phidal Publishing, Inc.
All rights reserved.
www.phidal.com

London Tour

These cars are ready to see London! Decorate the page with your stickers.

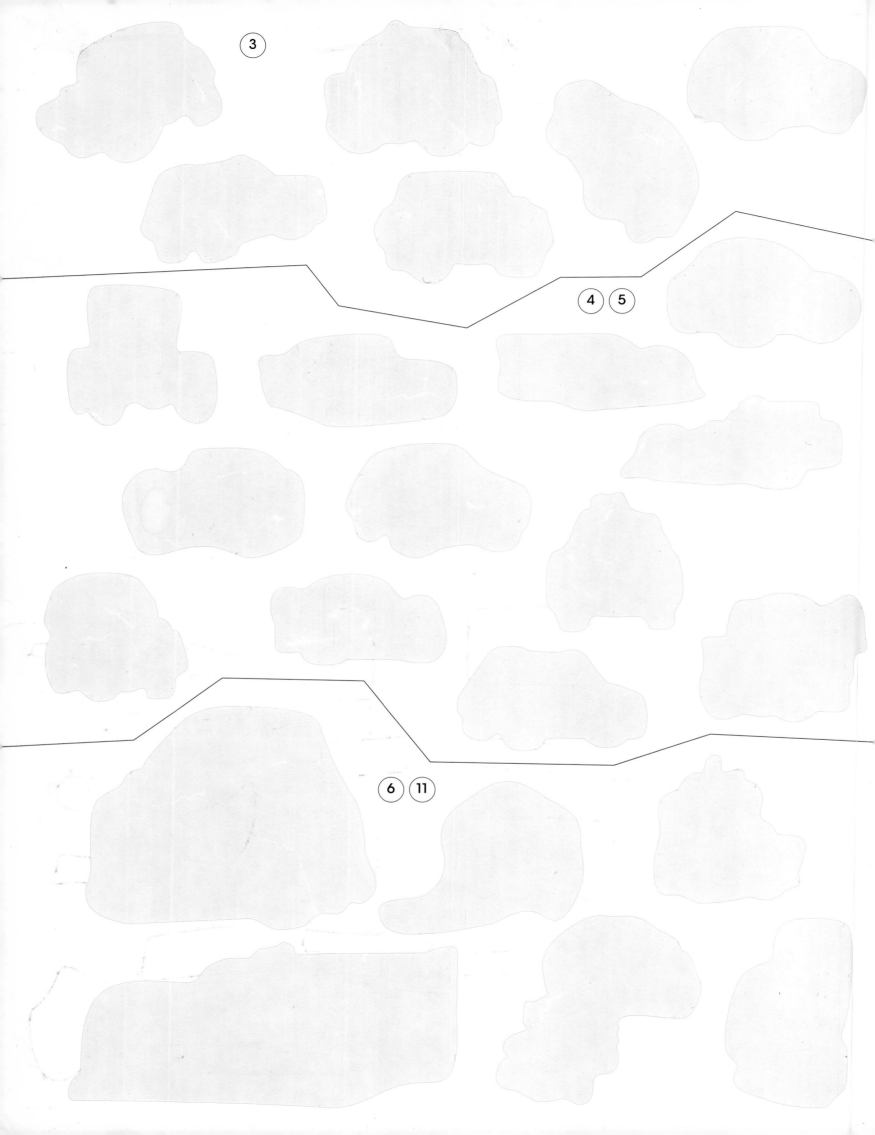

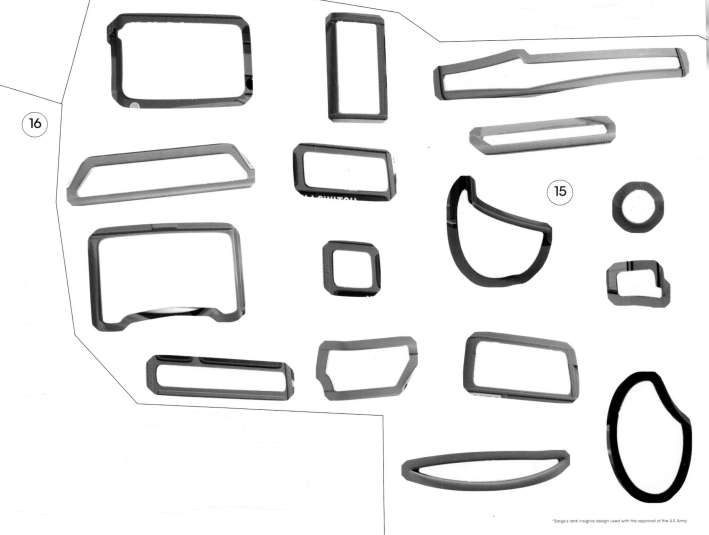

Unique Designs

Match the cars to their one-of-a-kind designs.

No Place Like Home

Place the stickers on the right shadows according to their home country.

Japan

United Kingdom

Italy

USA

France

Japan

Germany

Italy

Fill In the Blanks

Place your stickers over the shadows to make these vehicles complete.

Santa Ruotina

Uncle Topolino's village is beautiful! Make the bottom scene look like the top one.